# OLD TUATARA ⁹ᶜ

## by Joy Cowley

## illustrated by Clare Bowes

LEARNING
MEDIA®

Old Tuatara sat in the sun.

He sat and sat and sat.

"Asleep," said the fantail.

"Asleep," said the gull.

"Asleep," said the frog.

"Asleep," said the fly.

"Not asleep," said Old Tuatara.